CW00382344

Biology 1a — Human Biology
Page 1 — Diet and Metabolic Rate

Q1 A diet containing the right balance of different foods and the right amount of energy.

Q2 a) build, repair (in either order)
b) energy
c) warm, energy
d) minerals, tiny

Q3 a) speed, reactions
b) proportion of muscle to fat in the body, inherited factors, amount of exercise

Q4 a) Alice — she has a more active job, so needs more energy, so will have a higher metabolic rate.
b) David — he has more muscle than fat, so needs more energy, so will have a higher metabolic rate.

Page 2 — Factors Affecting Health

Q1 Eating too much fat or carbohydrate can cause obesity.
Not eating enough vitamins or minerals can cause deficiency diseases
Obesity can cause type 2 diabetes.

Q2 a) i) energy
ii) obesity
b) i) inherited
ii) heart disease

Q3 healthier, energy, fat, muscle, metabolic, less, obesity

Page 3 — Evaluating Food, Lifestyle and Diet

Q1 less, use, less, increases

Q2 a) Burger B
b) It contains more fat (including saturated fat) and carbohydrate than Burger A, and has a higher energy content.

Q3 a) Report B
b) It was published in a science journal. It used a large sample size.

Page 4 — Fighting Disease

Q1 microorganism, infectious
Q2 small, damaging, toxins, cells, copies, bursts, damage
Q3 a) They engulf and digest pathogens. They produce antitoxins.
b) white, antigen, antibodies, antigen, antibodies
Q4 Tiny bits of cells help the blood clot quickly to stop anything else getting in.

Page 5 — Fighting Disease — Vaccination

Q1 a) false
b) true
c) false
d) true

Q2 a) measles, mumps and rubella
b) 2. The inactive MMR pathogens had antigens on their surface.
3. John's white blood cells learnt to make the antibodies specific to these antigens.
4. If he is later infected with any of the MMR pathogens, John's white blood cells will quickly make antibodies specific to the antigens on that pathogen.
5. The antibodies will kill the pathogen so John won't get ill.

Q3 a) E.g. they've helped to control lots of infectious diseases that used to be common in the UK. / Epidemics can be prevented if lots of people are vaccinated.
b) E.g. Some people do not become immune after vaccination. You can sometimes have a bad reaction, e.g. swelling at the injection site.

Pages 6-7 — Fighting Disease — Drugs

Q1 A drug that kills bacteria.
Q2 reproduce, drugs, killing, mutations, resistant, antibiotic-resistant, natural selection
Q3 E.g. MRSA
Q4 A lid should be taped on the Petri dish to stop any microorganisms in the air getting in.
The Petri dish and culture medium should be sterilised to kill any unwanted microorganisms.
The inoculating loop should be sterilised by passing it through a flame.

Q5 a) The medicine doesn't kill the virus causing the cold — it just relieves the symptoms.
b) Colds are caused by a virus and antibiotics only kill bacteria.
c) Different antibiotics kill different types of bacteria, so a patient needs to be treated with the right antibiotic for it to have an effect.

Q6 a) It started to decrease in number.
b) i) 37 °C
ii) 25 °C, because harmful pathogens won't grow.
iii) 37 °C, so that microorganisms can grow a lot faster.

Page 8 — Fighting Disease — Past and Future

Q1 a) 12%
b) i) He asked all the doctors to wash their hands using antiseptic solution before seeing patients.
ii) The antiseptic solution killed bacteria on the doctors' hands.

Q2 a) Mutations
b) won't
c) immune
d) an epidemic
e) antigens
f) a pandemic

Q3 a) It's fallen dramatically.
b) i) E.g. by not overusing antibiotics.
ii) E.g. they're trying to develop new antibiotics that will kill resistant strains of bacteria.

Biology 1a — Human Biology

Pages 9-10 — The Nervous System

Q1 E.g. so they can react/respond to the changes in their surroundings.

Q2 Light receptor cells contain a nucleus, cytoplasm and a cell membrane.

Q3 hearing

Q4 a) five
b) receptors
c) balance, body position
d) skin, temperature
e) electrical
f) eye, light
g) CNS

Q5 a) central nervous system
b) brain and spinal cord

Q6 a) muscle
b) hormones

Q7 receptor, sensory neurone, CNS, motor neurone, effector

Q8 a) Chemical receptor. **Tongue** underlined.
b) Chemical receptor. **Nose** underlined.
c) Sound receptor. **Ears** underlined.
d) Pain receptor. **Skin** underlined.

Page 11 — Synapses and Reflexes

Q1 a) quickly
b) protect
c) without
d) neurones
e) chemicals

Q2 a) V = sensory neurone, W = synapse, X = relay neurone, Y = synapse, Z = motor neurone
b) electrically
c) i) effector
ii) contracting

Q3 The nerve signal is taken across the gap by chemicals. These chemicals set off a new electrical signal in the next neurone.

Page 12 — Hormones

Q1 chemical, glands, blood, target
Q2 a) e.g. FSH / LH
b) e.g. oestrogen
Q3 a) slower
b) longer
c) in a general way
d) on a precise area
Q4 a) blood
b) oestrogen
c) FSH
d) glands
e) LH

Page 13 — The Menstrual Cycle

Q1 FSH — pituitary gland
oestrogen — ovaries

Q2 a) FSH — causes an egg to mature in one of the ovaries
LH — causes the release of an egg from the ovaries
Oestrogen — inhibits FSH
b) FSH

Q3 a) & b)

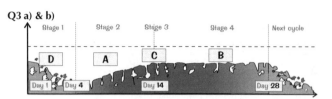

Pages 14-15 — Controlling Fertility

Q1 a) too low
b) stimulate
c) to get pregnant

Q2 contraceptive, high, progesterone, side effects, blood clots, lower, side effects

Q3 a) E.g. it's very effective at preventing pregnancy. It reduces the risk of getting some types of cancer.
b) Because it has fewer side effects.

Q4 The contraceptive pill — any two from e.g.: there's still a very slight chance of getting pregnant. / Causes side effects like headaches. / Doesn't protect against STDs.
FSH / LH — e.g. it doesn't always work / it can cause multiple pregnancies.

Q5 a) 2. The woman's eggs are collected from her ovaries and fertilised in a lab using a man's sperm.
3. The fertilised eggs are grown into embryos.
4. Once the embryos are tiny balls of cells, one or two of them are transferred to the woman's womb.
b) **Advantages** — It allows infertile couples to have children.
Disadvantages — There can be reactions to the hormones, e.g. vomiting. It may result in multiple births, which can be risky.

Pages 16-17 — Plant Hormones

Q1 a) false
b) false
c) true
d) true
e) false

Q2 B and E

Q3 Phototropism means growing in response to light. Geotropism (gravitropism) means growing in response to gravity.

Q4 shade, faster, towards, lower, faster, upwards, lower, slower, downwards

Q5 a) There was no change.
b) i) No auxin would have been able to move to the side in the shade.
ii) There is even distribution of auxin so no bending occurs.
c) E.g. Vicky could repeat the experiment to improve the reliability of the results.

Q6 a) it increased crop yield.
b) Plant growth hormones kill broad-leaved plants (the weeds) but not crops.

Pages 18-19 — Homeostasis

Q1 C — The maintenance of a 'constant internal environment'.

Q2 The enzymes in your body work best at about 37 °C.

Q3 a) Eating/drinking foods that are rich in simple carbohydrates, i.e. sugars.
b) To provide the body's cells with a constant supply of energy.

Biology 1b — Environment and Evolution

Q4 hot, sweat a lot, less, dark, less, concentrated
Q5 The following should be ticked:
Ronald loses salt in his sweat.
Ronald's kidneys remove salt from his blood.
Ronald gets rid of salt in his urine.
Q6 a) i) Skin — water is lost when we sweat.
   ii) Lungs — water is lost as we breathe.
   iii) Kidneys — water is lost as urine.
 b) i) More water. The exercise will increase his temperature, so he will have to sweat more to cool down.
   ii) More water. The exercise will make him breathe harder, so more water will be lost via the lungs.
   iii) Less water. More will be lost as sweat and in the breath, so to balance this the kidneys will give out less water in the urine.

Page 20 — Drugs

Q1 a) A chemical that alters the reactions in your body.
 b) i) You want a drug really badly. You can get withdrawal symptoms if the drug is not taken.
   ii) E.g. heroin
 c) To lower the risk of heart and circulatory disease.
Q2 a) E.g. steroids, stimulants
 b) They may not know all the health risks.
It makes sporting competitions unfair.
Q3 a) In the group that were given statins.
 b) Statins combined with lifestyle changes helps to reduce cholesterol levels more than just lifestyle changes alone.
 c) The group that wasn't given statins act as the control.

Page 21 — Testing Medicinal Drugs

Q1 1. Drug is tested on human cells and tissues
2. Drug is tested on live animals
3. Human volunteers are used to test the drug
Q2 sleeping pill, morning sickness, tested, unborn, arm, leg, banned, leprosy
Q3 a) E.g. to find the optimum dose / to test how well the drug works.
 b) A placebo is a substance that's like the drug being tested but contains no drug.
 c) A double blind trial is one where neither the scientist doing the test nor the patient knows whether they are getting a drug or a placebo.

Page 22 — Recreational Drugs

Q1 a) Liver disease, unconsciousness and addiction should be underlined.
 b) Cancer, addiction, lung disease should be underlined.
Q2 a) Any two from: e.g. for enjoyment / relaxation/stress relief.
 b) E.g. they can cause problems with the heart / circulatory system.
Q3 People are more likely to use cannabis than hard drugs.
Q4 a) Because so many more people take them.
 b) E.g. the NHS spends large amounts each year on treating patients with drinking-related problems.

Pages 23-25 — Mixed Questions — Biology 1a

Q1 a) In the blood.
 b) slow response, response lasts for a long time
 c) i) At the tips of the shoots and roots.
   ii) In shoots, auxin makes the cells grow faster. In roots, auxin slows cell growth.
   iii) E.g. weedkiller
Q2 a) 28 days
 b) An egg is released / ovulation.
 c) FSH / LH.
 d) It inhibits FSH, so no eggs mature.
Q3 true, false, false, true, false
Q4 a) i) Vitamins
   ii) Overeating
   iii) more
   iv) energy
 b) i) E.g. through the skin as sweat, via the lungs in breath, via the kidneys as urine.
   ii) more, sweat, less
Q5 Any three from, e.g: Whether it is published in a well-known science journal. / Whether it was written by a qualified person. / How large a sample was used. / Whether there have been other studies that have found similar results.
Q6 a) The sense organs are the ears, and they contain sound and balance receptors.
 b) i) Sensory neurones carry impulses from receptors to the CNS. Motor neurones carry impulses from the CNS to the effectors (muscles and glands).
   ii) synapse
 c) i) E.g. to increase muscle size
   ii) E.g. high blood pressure
Q7 a) The bacteria have been killed by the antibiotic.
 b) i) Antibiotic 3.
   ii) Flu and colds are caused by viruses but antibiotics don't kill viruses.

Biology 1b — Environment and Evolution

Pages 26-27 — Adaptations

Q1 a) hot
 b) cold
 c) dry
 d) salty
Q2 extremophiles, pressure, temperature
Q3 a) In the desert.
 b) i) E.g. the cactus has spines instead of leaves, because the small surface area reduces water loss.
   ii) E.g. the cactus has a thick stem where it can store water.
   iii) E.g. the cactus roots spread out over a large area to absorb water quickly.
Q4 a) i) white fur
   ii) It provides camouflage (white colour makes it hard to spot against a snowy background).
 b) It is a warning colour to scare off predators.
 c) E.g. poison in their stings.
Q5 a) The kangaroo rat.
 b) The polar bear.
 c) Less heat.
 d) It would be bigger than the polar bear's because the desert is very hot, so the kangaroo rat needs to lose more heat than the polar bear, which lives in a cold climate.

Biology 1b — Environment and Evolution

Pages 28-29 — Competition and Environmental Change

Q1 a)   Light — Plants
Minerals from the soil — Plants
Space — Plants and Animals
Water — Plants and Animals
Food — Animals
Mates — Animals
b)   The two species would have to compete for it.
c)   E.g. as a source of food.
Q2 a)   April
b)   Boxes ticked: Water temperature, Lower number of predator fish
Q3 a)

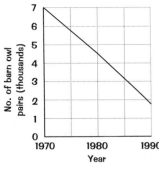

b)   The number of barn owls decreased between 1970 and 1990.
c)   E.g. fewer prey / more diseases / increase in competitors.
Q4 a)   It means a change in where the organism lives.
b)   The maximum height up the mountain where the snail was found has increased over the last 100 years.
c)   E.g. average rainfall

Page 30 — Measuring Environmental Change

Q1 a)   True
b)   True
c)   False
Q2 a)   Indicator species.
b)   Collect the samples in the same way
c)   Mayfly larvae prefer clean water.
d)   It leads to less oxygen in the water.
Q3 a)   1970.
b)   About 1 million tonnes.
c)   lichen

Page 31 — Pyramids of Biomass

Q1 a)   crab
b)   algae
c)   it decreases
Q2 a)   50 g
b) i)   C
ii)

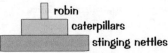

c)   The total mass of the organisms decreases at each step as shown by this pyramid.
d)   500 ÷ 25 = **20 g**

Page 32 — Energy Transfer and Decay

Q1 a)   true
b)   true
c)   false
d)   true
e)   false
f)   false
g)   true
Q2   Any two from:
Shredded waste — Shredding the waste gives more surface area for the microorganisms to work on.
Mesh sides — These allow contact with the air, so plenty of oxygen is available to help the microorganisms work faster.
Open top — This allows contact with the air, so plenty of oxygen is available to help the microorganisms work faster.
Q3   take, waste products, dead organisms, decay, microorganisms, soil, plants
Q4 a)   not stable
b)   stable
c)   not stable
d)   stable

Page 33 — The Carbon Cycle

Q1   carbon dioxide, photosynthesis, respire, microorganisms, eating, carbohydrates, waste, detritus
Q2   Plants use — carbon dioxide to build complex molecules.
Microorganisms release carbon dioxide by — respiration whilst decaying waste and dead tissue.
Animals and plants release — carbon dioxide through respiration.
Animals take in — carbon through feeding.
Plants take in carbon by — photosynthesis.
Q3 a)   fossil fuel (accept coal or oil)
b)   combustion / burning

Page 34 — Variation

Q1   have differences, genes, gametes, hair style, environment, a mixture of genetic and environmental factors, variation
Q2 a)   True
b)   False
c)   True
Q3 a)   Yes. Features like blood group are controlled by genes, so I would expect the girls to have the same blood group.
b)   The difference in weight must be due to environment (e.g. eating more or exercising less), because the twins have exactly the same genes.
c)   I don't think that birthmarks are caused by genes. Identical twins have exactly the same genes, so if Stephanie had a birthmark then Helen should too if it was genetic.

Page 35 — Genes and Chromosomes

Q1   nucleus, chromosomes, DNA, genes
Q2   gene, chromosome, nucleus, cell.
Q3 a)   nucleus
b)   chromosome
c)   part of DNA molecule
Q4   There are two chromosome 7s in a human nucleus, one from each parent.

Biology 1b — Environment and Evolution

Page 36 — Reproduction

Q1 a) two
b) gametes
c) identical
d) Sexual
e) asexual
Q2 a) clones
b) sperm
c) fuse together
Q3 a) Sexual reproduction

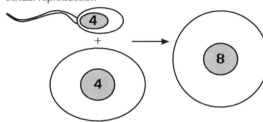

b) Asexual reproduction

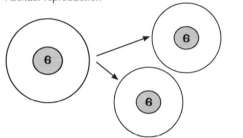

Q4 Asexual reproduction produces cells with identical genes to the parent cells.

Pages 37-38 — Cloning

Q1 Prize bull and cow are mated. → An embryo develops. → The embryo is then split many times, before any cells become specialised. → The embryos are put into the wombs of (implanted into) lots of other cows. → The embryos are clones, so all the baby calves will have the same genes.
Q2 a) You take a few plant cells and grow them into new plants — clones of the parent plant.
b) E.g. it's quick / it's cheap
Q3 implantation in an adult female = **D**
useful nucleus removed = **B**
putting the useful nucleus into an empty egg cell = **C**
Q4 genes, nucleus, egg, body, electric shock, dividing, clone
Q5 a) False
b) False
c) True
d) False
e) True
Q6 Any three from e.g.: cloning quickly gets you lots of ideal offspring. / Studying clones could help us understand some diseases. / Cloned organisms all have the same genes, so if a disease appears they could all be wiped out. / It's possible that cloned animals might not be as healthy as normal ones.

Page 39 — Genetic Engineering

Q1 A gene in human DNA → Enzymes cut the gene out of human DNA → Enzymes cut the DNA of bacteria → Then enzymes insert the useful gene into the DNA of bacteria
Q2 very early, develop, genetically modified, changed
Q3 viruses, insects, herbicides
Q4 Pro: GM crops can increase — the yield of a crop.
Con: GM crops might decrease — the number of flowers that live by the crops.
Pro: GM crops can include extra nutrients to — prevent deficiency diseases.
Con: some people worry GM crops aren't — safe to eat.

Page 40 — Evolution

Q1 A mutation is a change in an organism's DNA.
Useful characteristics may give an organism a better chance of surviving and reproducing.
A helpful mutation is more likely to be passed on to future generations by natural selection.
Q2 a) E.g. plants make their own food.
b) E.g. animals move about the place.
Q3 a) Rays and Sharks
b) They could be in competition.
Q4 2. Short-sighted birds in poor light didn't spot the stick-like moths.
3. So the stick-like moths were more likely to survive and reproduce.
4. Genes that made the moths look like sticks were more likely to be passed on to the next generation.

Page 41 — More About Evolution

Q1 A, D, E
Q2 Lamarck, more developed, longer, the next generation
Q3 People with dyed blue hair do not have children with blue hair.
Sheep whose tails are cut short give birth to lambs with full-length tails.
Q4 Any two from, e.g. because they have different beliefs / because they have been influenced by different people / because they think differently.

Pages 42-44 — Mixed Questions — Biology 1b

Q1 a) i) It increased.
ii) It stayed constant.
b) The goat.
c) natural selection
Q2 a) 19
b) 38 (19 + 19)
c)

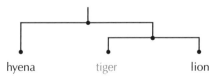

hyena   tiger   lion

Q3 a) Egg A.
b) The parents of egg A provided the genetic material that was inserted into egg B, so the toad inherited its features from these parents.
c) E.g. space and food
d) Species that are very sensitive to changes in their environment e.g. they can't live in some conditions.

Chemistry 1a — Products from Rocks

Q4 a) i) DNA
   ii) cut
   iii) enzymes
  b) asexual
Q5 a) 43 700 – 7500 = **36 200 kJ**
  b) Heat loss, waste materials, movement.
  c) B — Feeding
    C — Death and waste
    D — Respiration by microorganisms / detritus feeders
    E — Photosynthesis
    F — Respiration by plants
  d) The high temperature and good availability of oxygen will increase the rate of decomposition, as microorganisms work well in these conditions.

Chemistry 1a — Products from Rocks

Page 45 — Atoms and Elements

Q1 a) zero
  b) element
  c) protons, electrons (in either order)
  d) protons

Q2

Particle	Charge
Proton	+1
Neutron	0
Electron	-1

Q3 a) nucleus
  b) electron
  c) proton
  d) neutron
  e) proton

Q4

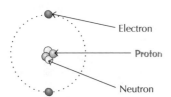

Electron
Proton
Neutron

Q5 copper and oxygen should be circled

Page 46 — The Periodic Table

Q1 a) A group in the periodic table is a **vertical** column of elements.
  b) Metals are on the **left** side of the periodic table.
  c) There are about 100 different **elements** in the periodic table.
  d) Each element has a different **symbol**.
  e) Elements in the same group have **similar** properties.
  f) The symbol for copper is **Cu** and the symbol for calcium is **Ca**.

Q2 a)

23
Na
11

  b) 11
  c) 11
  d) 23 – 11 = 12

Q3 a) The following should be ticked: **A** and **D**
  b) Group I, outer electrons, properties
Q4 a) false
  b) true
  c) true
  d) true

Pages 47-48 — Electron Shells

Q1 a) true
  b) false
  c) false
  d) false
Q2 E.g. The inner most electron shell should be filled first / there should be two electrons in the inner shell; The outer shell contains too many electrons, it only holds a maximum of 8 electrons.
Q3 a) 2,2
  b) 2,6
  c) 2,8,4
Q4 Missing words are: outer shell, unreactive, reactive, unreactive, reactive.
Q5 a) 2,8,7
  b)

  c) Its outer shell isn't full (it's keen to get an extra electron).

Q6

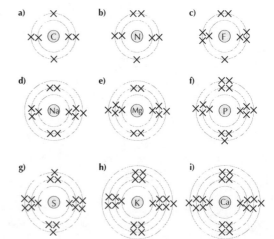

Page 49 — Compounds and Chemical Reactions

Q1 Missing words are: electrons, molecules, covalent.
Q2 a) True
  b) False
  c) True
Q3 a) 2
  b) 2
Q4 a) calcium oxide + water → calcium hydroxide
  b) Atoms aren't made or lost during a reaction. So, the mass of the reactants is the same as the mass of the products.
  c) 11 g (29 – 18 = 11).

Chemistry 1a — Products from Rocks

Pages 50-53 — Using Limestone

Q1   calcium carbonate
Q2 a) i)   calcium oxide, carbon dioxide
   ii)   thermal decomposition
  b) i)   False
   ii)   True
Q3 a)   calcium carbonate → calcium oxide + carbon dioxide
  b)   To neutralise soils that are acidic.
  c) i)   carbon dioxide
   ii)   The limewater goes cloudy.
Q4   The missing words are: limestone, mortar, concrete.
Q5 a)   carbon dioxide, water
  b)   magnesium carbonate + sulfuric acid → magnesium sulfate + carbon dioxide + water
  c)   Any two from, e.g. copper/zinc/calcium/sodium
  d)   Limestone is made of calcium carbonate. The calcium carbonate reacts with the acid in acid rain which erodes/ damages the building.
Q6   E.g. they provide jobs / bring money into the area.
Q7 a)   The limestone in the Peak District is very pure.
  b)   About 1.6 million tonnes (7.9 ÷ 5 = 1.58).
  c)   Any one from: it is used in agriculture / burned in lime kilns.
  d)   Any three from: increased traffic, spoiling the look of the landscape, putting off tourists, noise
  e) i)   canals and railways
   ii)   by road / by lorry
  f)   Answer will depend on student's opinion, but they are likely to say that they are against it because the article focuses on the problems associated with quarrying rather than the benefits it has.
  g)

Use	Percentage	Total amount quarried in tonnes
Aggregate (for road-building etc.)	52%	(52 ÷ 100) × 7 900 000 = 4 108 000
Cement	24%	(24÷ 100) × 7 900 000 = 1 896 000
Iron and steel making	2%	(2 ÷ 100) × 7 900 000 = 158 000
Chemicals and other uses	22%	(22 ÷ 100) × 7 900 000 = 1 738 000

Pages 54-56 — Getting Metals from Rocks

Q1   Missing words are: unreactive, compounds, ores.
Q2 a)   reduction
  b)   iron oxide + **carbon** → **iron** + carbon dioxide
  c)   electrolysis
Q3   **bodium**, carbon, **candium**, **antium**
Q4   Missing words are: electricity, liquid, negative.
Q5   A high temperature is needed to melt aluminium oxide. This uses a lot of energy which is expensive.
Q6 a)   Year 1
  b)   cost of extraction = 75/100 x £2.00 = £1.50, Year 6
Q7 a)   Because iron is more reactive than copper.
  b)   Because iron is less reactive than aluminium so it wouldn't be able to push the aluminium out.
Q8   copper, leaves, ash
Q9 a)   Bioleaching uses bacteria to separate copper from copper sulfide. The leachate (the solution produced by the process) contains copper. The copper can be extracted from the leachate, e.g. by filtering.
  b)   E.g. the supply of copper-rich ores is limited and the demand for copper is growing. / These alternative methods can extract copper from low-grade ores.

Page 57 — Impacts of Extracting Metals

Q1   Any three from: e.g. new jobs available for locals, improved local services, more money in local area, more goods made from the extracted metal are available, pollution such as dust and noise, habitat destruction, damage to the landscape.
Q2   E.g. there's only a fixed amount of metal in the Earth, which could one day run out if we don't recycle. If metal isn't recycled, it ends up in landfill sites, which take up space and pollute the surroundings. Mining and extracting new metals uses lots of energy / involves burning fossil fuels. Burning fossil fuels causes global warming, global dimming and acid rain.

Page 58 — Properties of Metals

Q1 a)   Metal 3 (because it has the best heat conduction, and is strong and resistant to corrosion).
  b)   Metal 2 (because it is the strongest, isn't too expensive and won't corrode too much). (Accept metal 3.)
  c)   Metal 1 (because it is most resistant to corrosion so it will last a long time).
Q2 a)   It can be bent to make pipes and tanks. It doesn't react with water.
  b)   It is a good conductor of electricity.
Q3 a)

Property	Aluminium	Titanium
Density	**low**	**low**
Strength	low	high
Corrosion resistance	**high**	**high**

  b)   transition metals

Page 59 — Alloys

Q1   Missing words are: pure, properties, alloys.
Q2 a)   True
  b)   False
  c)   True
  d)   False
  e)   True
Q3

Metal / Alloy — **Property**

low-carbon steel — brittle
iron from a blast furnace — doesn't corrode
high-carbon steel — easily shaped
stainless steel — very hard

Q4   It makes the gold harder.

Chemistry 1a — Products from Rocks

Page 60 — Fractional Distillation of Crude Oil

Q1 a) Crude oil is a **mixture** of different molecules.

b) Most of the compounds in crude oil are **hydrocarbon** molecules.

c) The molecules in crude oil **aren't** chemically bonded to each other.

d) Physical methods **can** be used to separate out the molecules in crude oil.

Q2

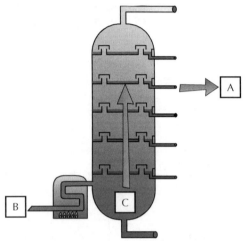

Q3 Each fraction contains molecules of a similar size / with a similar number of carbon atoms.

Page 61 — Properties and Uses of Crude Oil

Q1 a) C_nH_{2n+2} should be ticked.

b)

1.	2.	3.
H | H–C–H | H	H H | | H–C–C–H | | H H	H H H | | | H–C–C–C–H | | | H H H
methane	**ethane**	**propane**

c) Alkanes are saturated hydrocarbons.

Q2 a) The longer the alkane molecule the **more** viscous (gloopy) it is

b) The shorter the alkane molecule the **lower** its boiling point.

c) The shorter the alkane molecule the **more** flammable it is.

Q3 They would boil when the engine got hot / could catch fire easily.

Page 62 — Using Crude Oil as a Fuel

Q1 Missing words are: fractions, industry, non-renewable, renewable.

Q2 Burning: e.g. burning crude oil is thought to cause global warming, global dimming and acid rain.
Transporting crude oil across the sea in tankers: e.g. when oil is transported by ship there is the possibility of spills into the sea. Crude oil is poisonous to birds and sea creatures.

Q3 a) E.g. wind power, solar power, tidal power

b) E.g. most technology around today is set up to use crude oil fractions as fuel so they're often the cheapest and easiest things to use. / We need more energy than can currently be created using alternatives alone. / Crude oil fractions are often more reliable than some alternatives, e.g. solar and wind power won't work without the right weather conditions.

Pages 63-64 — Environmental Problems

Q1 In clouds sulfur dioxide reacts with water to make... sulfuric acid.
Acid rain kills trees and... makes lakes acidic.
Sulfur dioxide is produced by burning fuels which contain... sulfur.
Limestone buildings and statues are affected by... acid rain.
The main cause of acid rain is... sulfur dioxide.

Q2 Any two from:
Removing the sulfur from the fuel before it is burnt. / Using less fossil fuels. / Removing sulfur dioxide from the waste gases after fuels are burnt, e.g. in power station chimneys.

Q3 a) Carbon monoxide is formed when there is not enough oxygen for a hydrocarbon fuel to burn completely.

b) carbon

Q4 a) The combustion of hydrocarbons gives out heat.

b) carbon dioxide and water

Q5 a) false

b) true

c) true

d) false

e) false

Q6 a) hydrocarbon + **oxygen** → water + carbon dioxide + **carbon monoxide + carbon**

b) Because particles of soot (carbon) are released.

Pages 65-68 — More Environmental Problems

Q1 Global dimming is caused by particles of soot and ash.

Q2 a) The percentage of carbon dioxide in the atmosphere is increasing at an increasing rate.

b) The burning of fossil fuels.

c) It's causing the average temperature to increase.

Q3 a) water

b) Any one from: e.g. when hydrogen is used as a fuel no carbon dioxide is produced so it doesn't contribute to global warming. / It doesn't produce particles so it doesn't cause global dimming. / It doesn't produce sulfur dioxide so it doesn't cause acid rain.

c) Any three from e.g. you need a special, expensive engine. / Hydrogen isn't widely available. / You still need to use energy from another source to make hydrogen (e.g. from fossil fuels). / Hydrogen is hard to store.

Q4 plant material, carbon neutral, water, land, engines

Q5 a) Any three from: e.g. recycling metals, avoiding foods that have travelled a long way, saving electricity by turning lights off, not leaving electrical devices on stand-by, not flying (using other types of transport that use less fossil fuels), etc.

b) Answer will depend on student's opinion — may argue that everyone who lives on Earth and uses its resources has a responsibility to try and prevent environmental damage. Alternatively, may suggest that new technologies will be able to prevent damage.

Chemistry 1b — Oils, Earth and Atmosphere

Q6 a) Recycled cooking oil
b) Climate change might slow down. Spills would be less harmful to the environment.
c) It has reduced the tax on biodiesel and increased the tax on normal diesel.
d) The Government would get less money from fuel tax.
e) E.g. you don't need to get a diesel car modified. Biodiesel may cost slightly more but the Government is actually making less money on it than it does on normal diesel.

Pages 69-71 — Mixed Questions — Chemistry 1a

Q1 a) **A** should be ticked.
b) The following should be ticked:
Metals are generally strong but also malleable.
Metals conduct electricity well.
Properties of a metal can be altered by mixing it with another metal to form an alloy.
c) i) R.
ii) The material needs to be as light and as strong as possible with a high melting point and a reasonable price.
Q2 a) You could get oil spills, which damage the environment.
b) Any one from: e.g. global dimming / global warming / acid rain
Q3 a) There is a limited amount of metals in the Earth.
b) i) It is purified by electrolysis.
ii) E.g. easily bent, good conductor of electricity.
c) Aluminium is more reactive than carbon, and so cannot be extracted by reduction with carbon.
Q4 a) The following can be in any order:
Petrol has a lower boiling point than diesel. Petrol is more flammable (ignites more easily) than diesel. Petrol is less viscous (is runnier) than diesel.
b)

Fuel	Engine needs to be converted	Burning releases carbon dioxide
Ethanol	Yes	Yes
Hydrogen gas	Yes	No
Biodiesel	No	Yes

Q5 a) 20
b)

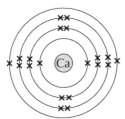

Q6 a) i)

calcium carbonate →(+ HEAT) **calcium oxide** →(+ WATER) calcium hydroxide

ii) E.g. neutralising acidic soil in fields / acidity in lakes.
b)

Limestone →(heat with clay) **cement** →(add sand and aggregate) **concrete**

c) sand and water
d) acid rain

Chemistry 1b — Oils, Earth and Atmosphere

Page 72 — Cracking Crude Oil

Q1 shorter, petrol, diesel, long, high, catalyst, molecules, cracking
Q2 a) E.g. fuels
b) Cracking is a thermal decomposition reaction.
Q3 nonane → octane + ethene
Q4 1. The long-chain molecules are heated.
2. They are vaporised (turned into a gas).
3. The vapour is passed over a catalyst at a high temperature.
4. The molecules are cracked on the surface of the catalyst.

Pages 73-74 — Alkenes and Ethanol

Q1 C_nH_{2n}
Q2 a) C_2H_4
b)

$$\underset{H}{\overset{H}{\diagdown}}C=C\underset{H}{\overset{H}{\diagup}}$$

c) Propene
Q3 Missing words are: decolourise, orange, colourless.
Q4 a) False
b) True
c) True
d) False
Q5 a) A
b) Method A — Uses yeast.
Method B — Uses a catalyst.
c) Any two from:
Needs lower temperatures so is cheaper. Can use simpler equipment. Uses sugar which is often grown as a major crop. Sugar is a renewable resource.
d) The ethanol produced is not very concentrated so it needs to be distilled. It needs to be purified.
Q6 Ethene from crude oil is a non-renewable resource and will one day run out.

Pages 75-76 — Using Alkenes to Make Polymers

Q1 The monomer of poly(ethene) is ethene.
Q2 Any three from:
e.g. plastic bags, waterproof coatings for fabrics, tooth fillings, hydrogel wound dressings, memory foam, packaging materials
Q3 Missing words are: rot, landfill, reuse, crude oil, expensive.
Q4 New biodegradable plastics are being made by adding cornstarch to polymers.
Q5 Cracking: Splits less useful crude oil fractions into alkenes. Turns longer molecules into shorter ones.
Polymerisation: Turns alkenes into polymers. Turns shorter molecules into longer ones.
Q6

$$n\begin{pmatrix} CH_3 & H \\ | & | \\ C=C \\ | & | \\ H & H \end{pmatrix} \longrightarrow \begin{pmatrix} CH_3 & H \\ | & | \\ C-C \\ | & | \\ H & H \end{pmatrix}_n$$

many propene molecules   poly(propene)

Chemistry 1b — Oils, Earth and Atmosphere

Pages 77-78 — Plant Oils

Q1 a) Missing words are: crushed, pressed
b) Any two from: e.g. in food / in cooking / as a fuel
c) water and impurities
Q2 Vegetable oils provide loads of energy.
They provide us with nutrients.
Q3 a) False
b) True
c) False
d) False
Q4 a) biodiesel
b) They contain lots of energy.
Q5 a) i) Martin's.
ii) E.g. His method is more detailed. He gives accurate quantities of oil and bromine water. He labels his equipment so there is less opportunity for mistakes. He writes down the results after each individual experiment.
b) A: yes
B: no
C: yes
Q6 a) saturated
b) They increase the amount of cholesterol in the blood. Cholesterol can block arteries and lead to heart disease.

Page 79 — Emulsions

Q1 a) Oils don't dissolve in water.
b) Emulsions are thicker than both water and oil.
c) In an emulsion the droplets of one liquid are suspended in another liquid.
d) Emulsions like salad dressing are good at coating foods.
Q2 a) Any two from: e.g. salad dressing / whipped cream / ice cream.
b) Any one from: e.g. paint / moisturiser.
Q3 a) Emulsifiers make emulsions more stable and stop them from separating out.
b) i) Any one from: e.g. they give food a better texture, they give emulsions a longer shelf life.
ii) Some people are allergic to certain emulsifiers.

Pages 80-81 — Plate Tectonics

Q1 continental drift, fossils, land bridges, Pangaea, spinning.
Q2 True, True, False, True
Q3 Fossils found on either side of the Atlantic were almost the same.
The coastlines of South America and Africa seem to match.
Rocks with matching layers have been found in different countries.
Q4 a) Tidal forces and the Earth's spinning.
b) E.g. he had used dodgy data and made some unbelievable predictions about how fast the plates were moving apart. His idea sounded so strange.
c) Scientists eventually found evidence to support Wegener's theory on the ocean floor.
This evidence proved that he was right about some things in his theory.

Pages 82-83 — The Earth's Structure

Q1 1. crust
2. mantle
3. core
Q2 The main earthquake zones are along the plate boundaries.
Q3 1.6 × 10 000 = 16 000 cm = 0.16 km
Q4 Crust — Thinnest of the Earth's layers
Mantle — Slowly flowing, mostly solid layer that plates float on
Convection current — Caused by heat from radioactive decay in the mantle
Tectonic plates — Large pieces of crust and upper mantle
Earthquakes — Caused by sudden movements of plates
Q5 E.g. tectonic plates stay still for a long time and then suddenly lurch forwards. It's impossible to know exactly when they'll move.

Pages 84-85 — The Evolution of the Atmosphere

Q1 a) True
b) False
c) True
d) True
Q2 The statements should be in this order (from the top of the timeline):
1. The atmosphere is about 80% nitrogen and 20% oxygen.
2. Green plants and algae evolve over the Earth. The green plants and algae absorb some of the carbon dioxide and produce oxygen by photosynthesis. A lot of the carbon dioxide also dissolves into the oceans.
3. Water vapour condenses to form oceans.
4. The Earth cools down slightly. A thin crust forms. There are lots of volcanoes erupting.
5. The Earth's surface is molten — it's so hot that any atmosphere just 'boils away' into space.
Q3 Largest sector is Nitrogen, second largest is Oxygen, smallest is Carbon dioxide and other gases.
Q4 a) Burning fossil fuels
b) i) Generally increased (although it has gone up and down).
ii) Global warming
Q5 acidic, coral, carbon dioxide

Pages 86-88 — Mixed Questions — Chemistry 1b

Q1 a)

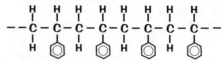

b) Unlike alkanes, alkenes are unsaturated because they have double bonds.
Q2 a) cracking
b) Name: poly(styrene)

c) E.g. it's difficult to get rid of them / they fill up landfill sites.
Q3 a) False
b) True
c) True
d) False

Physics 1a — Energy

Q4 a) Rapeseed is crushed and then pressed between metal plates to squeeze the oil out.

b) Rapeseed oil will turn bromine water from orange to colourless.

c) E.g. heart disease.

d) An emulsifier stops the oil and water in an emulsion from separating out / makes an emulsion more stable.

Q5 a) surface, evidence, tectonic plates, tidal forces, convection currents

b) Earthquakes and volcanic eruptions

Q6 a) There was no oxygen.

b) i) Green plants and algae.

ii) The oceans absorbed CO_2.

c) i) increasing, carbon dioxide, burning

ii) global warming

d) i) True

ii) True

iii) False

Physics 1a — Energy

Pages 89-90 — Heat Radiation

Q1 a) True

b) True

c) False

d) True

e) False

f) False

Q2 emit / absorb, emit / absorb, more, less, faster, hot

Q3 a) Dark, matt surfaces are **good** absorbers and **good** emitters of infrared radiation.

b) The best surfaces for radiating infrared are **good** absorbers and **good** emitters.

c) Light, shiny surfaces are **poor** absorbers and **poor** emitters of infrared radiation.

d) Light, shiny surfaces are **good** reflectors of infrared radiation.

e) The best surfaces for solar hot water panels are **good** absorbers and **good** emitters.

Q4 a) False

b) True

c) True

d) False

Q5 Paint the radiator matt black.
Put something shiny between the radiator and the roof.

Q6 Flask B will cool fastest because there is a larger temperature difference between the water and the air in the box.

Page 91 — Kinetic Theory

Q1

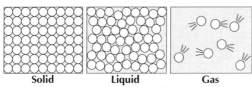

Gas — There are almost no forces of attraction between the particles.
Liquid — There are weak forces of attraction between the particles.
Solid — There are strong forces of attraction holding the particles close together.

Q2 a) True

b) False

c) True

d) True

e) False

f) True

Q3 1. Before being heated, the particles in a solid only vibrate a little bit.
2. When a solid is heated, the particles gain energy.
3. As the particles gain energy, they are able to move more.
4. Eventually the particles have enough energy to move past each other and the solid becomes a liquid.

Page 92 — Conduction

Q1 a) True

b) False

c) True

d) False

Q2 good, free, faster, collide, energy, carry

Q3 a) Insulator

b) Conductor

c) Conductor

d) Conductor

Q4 The piece of wood feels quite warm because wood is a poor conductor, so it does not conduct much heat energy away from George's hand. The metal spoon feels colder because metal is a good conductor, so it conducts heat energy away from his hand very quickly.

Page 93 — Convection

Q1 a) True

b) False

c) True

d) False

Q2

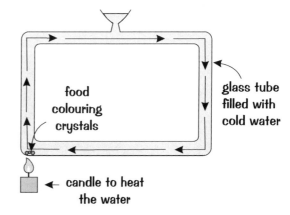

Q3 The very bottom of a hot water tank stays cold... because water doesn't conduct much heat.
Warm air rises... because it is less dense than cool air.
Water becomes less dense when it is heated... because the water particles have more energy and move further apart.

Q4 energy, bigger, density, cooler, convection

Physics 1a — Energy

Page 94 — Condensation and Evaporation

Q1 cools, energy, forces, liquid
Q2 a) True
b) True
c) False
Q3 a) evaporation
b) When sweat evaporates, it has a cooling effect — it **decreases** your body temperature.
c) E.g. The liquid particles of sweat on your skin absorb heat energy from your body. The particles of sweat with the highest energy are the first to evaporate. When they do, the particles that are left have a lower average energy and the average temperature of your body goes down.
Q4 a) E.g. Put tea in a slimmer cup so that the surface area of the tea is reduced. / Have colder tea. / Reduce the airflow over the tea.
b) E.g. Increase the temperature of the window space. / Decrease the surface area of the window exposed (e.g. by drawing the curtains).

Pages 95-96 — Rate of Heat Transfer

Q1 Cooling fins.
The engine is made of metal.
The engine has a large surface area.
Q2 a) To maximise the amount of heat transfer.
b) Metal is a good conductor so it will conduct heat away from the radiator much faster than air, as air is an insulator.
c) B (because although it has the same surface area, it has a smaller volume.)
Q3 Air is a very good **insulator** of heat energy. When you get cold, your body hairs **stand on end** so they can **trap a thicker layer of air** around your body. By doing this, the amount of heat you lose to your surroundings by convection and **conduction**. Wearing a coat also helps you keep warm in this way.
Q4 1. Plastic cap filled with cork — reduces conduction (because plastic and cork are insulators).
2. Shiny mirrored surfaces — reduce radiation.
3. Vacuum (gap between walls of bottle) — reduces conduction and convection.
4. Sponge — reduces conduction.
5. Air — reduces conduction.
Q5 a) Fox A
b) i) The desert fox has **large** ears that have a large surface area, allowing the fox to lose heat easily by radiation. This helps the fox avoid overheating in a hot climate.
ii) The Arctic fox has **small** ears that have a small surface area to minimise heat losses by radiation. This helps the fox to keep warm in a cold environment.

Pages 97-98 — Energy Efficiency in the Home

Q1 Through the roof — e.g. loft insulation.
Through the walls — e.g. cavity wall insulation.
From the hot water tank — e.g insulating hot water tank jacket.
Q2 fibreglass, radiation, wall, gaps, conduction
Q3 a) Payback time = 200 ÷ 100 = 2 years.
b) Yes, because loft insulation is more cost-effective — it has a shorter payback time.

Q4 Shona and Alison are right.
(Shona is right — a method that pays for itself faster will start saving you money sooner.
Alison is right — good value means getting a good effect from the money spent.
Tim is wrong — cheap or badly installed insulation might not work very well.
Meena is wrong — cost-effectiveness means getting a good energy saving per pound spent.)
Q5 a) How effective a material is as an insulator.
b) Gary should buy brand **A** because it has a lower U-value — the lower the U-value, the better the material is as an insulator, so heat transfer will be less.

Page 99 — Specific Heat Capacity

Q1 energy, 1 kg, 1 °C
Q2 a) $E = m \times c \times \theta$
b) m = 3 kg
c = 4200 J/kg/°C
θ = 10 °C
$E = 3 \times 4200 \times 10 = \textbf{126 000 J}$ (= 126 kJ)
Q3 a) Concrete
b) E.g.
1. It has a really high specific heat capacity so it can store large amounts of heat.
2. It can be easily pumped around pipes because it is a liquid.

Page 100 — Energy Transfer

Q1 Conservation, transferred, dissipated, created
Q2 a) **chemical energy** → heat and light energy.
b) electrical energy → **sound and heat energy**.
c) **electrical energy** → **light and heat energy**.
Q3 Electric fan — kinetic energy
Iron — heat energy
Bedside table lamp — light energy
Q4 a) Gravitational potential energy.
b) The gravitational potential energy is transferred into kinetic energy as it falls downwards.
Q5 a) E.g. loudspeaker or buzzer/bell
b) E.g. solar cell
c) E.g. hairdryer or electric fan heater

Pages 101-102 — Efficiency of Machines

Q1 transfer, useful, heat, surroundings
Q2 a) 100 J
b) 5 J
c) 100 J – 5 J = **95 J**
Q3

	Total Energy In (J)	Useful Energy Out (J)	Efficiency
1	2000	1500	**0.75**
2	4000	2000	**0.50**
3	4000	1000	**0.25**

Q4 Efficiency = useful power out ÷ total power in
= 1200 ÷ 2000 = 0.6
Efficiency = 0.6 × 100% = **60%**

Physics 1a — Energy

Q5 a) Some of the waste heat energy could be used to warm the air that's used to warm the passengers.

b) Using a heat exchanger makes a car **more** efficient because more of the total energy put in is converted into useful energy. However, even with the heat exchanger, the car will **never** be 100% efficient. Some energy will always be **lost** as heat and sound.

Q6 a) E.g. any two from: Longer life. / Cheaper to run OR uses less energy/electricity. / Cheaper to buy per year of its lifetime. (Or other sensible answers.)

b) E.g. Cheaper to buy.

Pages 103-104 — Energy Transformation Diagrams

Q1 a) 200 J ÷ 20 squares = 10 J per square

b) 200 – 50 = 150 J

Q2

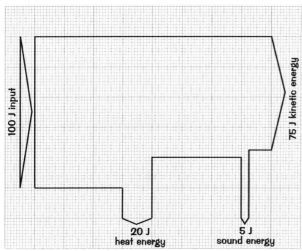

Q3 1. The input energy is not shown clearly.
The 100 J kinetic energy should be shown as input energy and the arrow should be the other way around.
2. The size of the arrow for the heat energy is the wrong size. For 25 J, the arrow should be 5 squares wide (as 1 square = 5 J).

Q4 a) 100 J heat + 40 J gravitational potential energy = **140 J**

b) 60 J

c) Efficiency = 60 ÷ 200 = **0.3**.

Pages 105-106 — The Cost of Electricity

Q1 a) electrical

b) how fast

c) watts

d) how long, power

e) joules

Q2 1350 J

Q3 a) Energy used = 2 kW × 3 hours = **6 kWh**.

b) Cost of energy = 14p/kWh × 6 kWh = **84p**.

Q4 Energy transferred = 0.1 kW × 10 h = 1 kWh, so the cost is **11.3p**.

Q5 a) 34783 – 34259 = **524 kWh**.

b) 524 × 10p = 5240p = **£52.40**.

Q6 a) Convert 60 W to kW first: 60 ÷ 1000 = 0.06 kW.
A 0.06 kW lamp on for 9 h uses 0.06 × 9 = **0.54 kWh**.

b) Convert 15 minutes into hours first: 15 ÷ 60 = 0.25 hours.
An 8 kW shower on for 0.25 h uses 8 × 0.25 = **2 kWh**.

c) An 8 kW shower being used for 15 minutes.

Q7 a) Difference between meter readings
= 13598.63 – 13592.43 = **6.2 kWh**.

b) Cost of energy = 11p/kWh × 6.2 kWh
= 68.2p = **68p to the nearest penny**.

Page 107 — Choosing Electrical Appliances

Q1 a) E.g. It's cheaper to buy. / It weighs less. / It has a foldable handle so it won't take up much room in a suitcase.

b) E.g. It's more powerful. / You can change the speed and temperature settings.

Q2 The following two sentences should be ticked:
There might not be an electricity supply where they are camping.
Wind-up radios don't have power cords that might get in the way.

Q3 Difference in energy used = 17 – 16 = 1 kWh.
So June would save = 1 × 12 = **12p**.

Q4 E.g. any two from: can be used to power X-ray machines / refrigeration of medicines/vaccines / can power lighting/ equipment for operations / refrigeration of food.

Pages 108-109 — Mixed Questions — Physics 1a

Q1 a) conduction

b) Brand B

c) cools, energy, attraction, liquid

Q2 a) Heat radiation from the Bunsen burner is transferred to the thermometers by being **absorbed** and then **emitted** by the metal plates. Thermometer **A** is heated to a higher temperature. This is because the metal plate in front of it is coated with a **matt black** surface which is a good **absorber** and emitter of heat radiation.

b) chemical energy → **heat energy + light energy + sound energy**

c) E.g. Metals have free electrons which can carry heat energy quickly due to their movement and collisions. Also, there are no large gaps between particles in a solid metal, making conduction easier.

Q3 a) i) First convert minutes to hours: 45 ÷ 60 = 0.75 hours.
Sander A: Energy (in kWh) = Power (in kW) × Time (in h)
= 0.36 × 0.75 = **0.27 kWh**.

ii) First convert minutes to hours: 30 ÷ 60 = 0.5 hours.
Sander B: Energy = 0.4 × 0.5 = **0.2 kWh**.

b) 4p (0.27 × 15 = 4.05p)).

Q4 a)

Work needed	Annual Saving (£)	Cost of work (£)	Payback time (years)
Hot water tank jacket	15	15	**1**
Draught-proofing	80	100	**1.25**
Cavity wall insulation	70	560	**8**
Thermostatic controls	30	120	**4**

b) Hot water tank jacket

c) Draught proofing saves £80 per year.
Over 5 years that is a saving of 5 × £80 = £400
But there is an initial cost of £100
So total saving over 5 years = £400 – £100 = **£300**

Physics 1b — Electricity and Waves

Physics 1b — Electricity and Waves

Page 110 — Energy Sources & Power Stations

Q1 a) Non-renewable — they all do damage to the environment, they will all run out one day.
Renewable — they will never run out, some of them don't always work because of the weather.

b) Coal: non-renewable
Wind: renewable
Geothermal: renewable
Nuclear: non-renewable

Q2 a) 1. The fossil fuel is burned to release heat.
2. Water is heated in a boiler and turned to steam.
3. Hot steam rushes through a turbine and makes it spin.
4. The spinning turbine makes the generator spin too.
5. Electricity is produced by the spinning generator.

b) Coal, oil and natural gas.

Q3 steam, turbine, electricity, burnt, fission, plutonium

Page 111 — Renewable Energy Sources (1)

Q1 a) D
b) A
c) A
d) A
e) D
f) A

Q2 a) coasts
b) directly, generator
c) harmful
d) fuel, high
e) pollution, wildlife, windy

Q3 The cost of connecting the remote farm to the National Grid would be too large compared with the value of the electricity generated.

Pages 112-113 — Renewable Energy Sources (2)

Q1 Big coal-fired power stations generate energy... all the time.
Pumped storage systems don't generate electricity, but deliver energy that they... have previously stored.
Hydroelectric power stations generate electricity... when it is needed.

Q2 a) falling
b) dam, turbines
c) demand, release
d) small, high, expensive

Q3 1. At night big power stations make more electricity than is needed.
2. Spare electricity is used to pump water from reservoirs at a low level to others at a high level.
3. Water at a high level stores energy until it is needed.
4. At peak times, when demand is the highest, water is allowed to flow downhill, powering turbines and generating electricity.

Q4 a) E.g. I agree... there are no gases released into the atmosphere when the electricity is being generated.
E.g. I disagree... they do cause visual pollution.

b) E.g. I agree... there are no fuel costs.
E.g. I disagree... they are expensive to set up.

c) E.g. I agree... the dams can look ugly and ruin wildlife habitats.
E.g I disagree... they are often built in remote places where there aren't many people living, so it doesn't affect as many people's view as other types of power stations.

d) E.g. I agree... water can be released to power the generators when it's needed most.
E.g I disagree... it isn't a very reliable source of energy when there is a drought.

Page 114 — Renewable Energy Sources (3)

Q1 a) Tidal
b) Wave
c) Tidal
d) Wave
e) Tidal

Q2 a) When the tide comes in, it fills up the estuary and drives the turbines.
b) Tidal power generally has **low** running costs.
c) E.g. barrages can look ugly, barrages can damage wildlife habitats.

Q3 a) 1. A wave moves water upwards, forcing air out towards a turbine.
2. The moving air makes the turbine spin.
3. The spinning turbine drives a generator.
4. The spinning generator makes electricity.
5. The water goes down again.
6. Air is sucked downwards, spinning the turbine the other way and generating more power.

b) E.g. any two from the following: High initial costs. / Spoiling the view. / Can be unreliable because it depends on winds. / It is currently only suitable for small-scale use.

Page 115 — Renewable Energy Sources (4)

Q1 fossil fuels, burnt, water, turbines, quick, waste
Q2 They won't run out — more can always be made.
Q3 E.g. In some **volcanic** areas, hot water and **steam** rise to the surface. This steam can be used to drive **turbines** which turn generators and produce electricity.

Q4 a) False
b) False
c) False
d) True

Page 116 — Energy Sources and the Environment

Q1 Acid rain — sulfur dioxide formed by burning oil and coal.
Climate change — releasing carbon dioxide by burning fossil fuels.
Dangerous radioactive waste — using nuclear power.
Spoiling of natural landscapes — coal mining OR sulfur dioxide formed by burning oil and coal.

Q2 Answer will depend on student's opinion but should include an explanation of their reasoning, e.g. Lisa because nuclear power produces long-lasting, dangerous, radioactive waste.
Or Ben because nuclear power is carefully controlled to reduce any dangers. Also, nuclear power doesn't produce any carbon dioxide, whereas using fossil fuels adds to the carbon dioxide in the atmosphere, leading to climate change / an increased greenhouse effect / global warming.

Physics 1b — Electricity and Waves

Q3 a) Carbon capture and storage (CCS) is used to **reduce** the amount of carbon dioxide (CO_2) released into the atmosphere. This helps **reduce** the strength of the greenhouse effect. CCS works by collecting the CO_2 from power stations **before** it is released into the atmosphere.

b) E.g. in empty gas fields/oil fields, like those under the North Sea.

Q4 Plants that are used to produce biofuels (or to feed animals that produce biofuels) take in CO_2 from the atmosphere as they grow. Burning the biofuel puts the carbon back into the atmosphere as carbon dioxide, so overall there is no change to the amount of CO_2 in the atmosphere.

Pages 117-118 — Comparison of Energy Resources

Q1 gas

Q2 renewable, non-renewable, unreliable, pollution, run out, safe, expensive

Q3 a) Non-renewable

b) Non-renewable energy resources have higher costs as they require a fuel that has to be mined and transported. Renewable energy resources don't usually use a fuel.

Q4 E.g. They're more reliable as they don't depend on the weather like other renewable energy resources do.

Q5 a) E.g. Gas will run out eventually. / Burning gas causes atmospheric pollution and contributes to the global warming.

b) E.g. High set-up costs. / High maintenance and/or decommissioning costs. / Long set-up times. / Dangerous radioactive waste. / Risk of accidents.

c) E.g. It's dependent on the weather. / Only works when the wind is blowing. / Unreliable. / Visual pollution. / Spoils the view. / Noise pollution.

d) E.g. High set-up costs.

Q6 a) Shutting down the power station so that it is no longer used to generate electricity.

b) Nuclear power stations

Q7 Answer will depend on student's opinion. 'I agree' could be backed up by saying that sea levels change in a predictable and reliable way, twice every day. 'I disagree' could be backed up by saying that there are only a few suitable estuaries, or that the height of the tides isn't always the same, so at low tides there is not as much energy available as when there are high tides.

Pages 119-120 — Electricity and the National Grid

Q1 1. Electrical energy is generated in power stations.
2. The voltage of the supply is raised.
3. An electrical current flows through power cables across the country.
4. The voltage of the supply is reduced.
5. Mrs Miggins boils the kettle for tea.

Q2 a) Underground cables
b) Overhead cables
c) Overhead cables
d) Overhead cables
e) Underground cables
f) Overhead cables

Q3 a) i) power station
ii) step-up transformer
iii) pylons
iv) step-down transformer

b) It is **cheaper** to use high voltages for transmission, even though the equipment is expensive. This is because at higher voltages **less** energy is wasted as heat. This saves **more** money than the cost of the equipment.

Q4 a) The National Grid transmits energy at high voltage and **low current**.

b) A step-up transformer is used to **increase** the voltage of the supply (OR reduce the **current**) before electricity is transmitted.

c) Using a **low current** (OR high **voltage**) makes sure there is not much energy wasted.

Q5 a) Consumer energy demands are increasing.

b) To meet consumer energy demands in the future, the National Grid could **increase** the amount of electricity they supply, e.g. by building more power stations. Another way of matching supply with demand would be if consumers **reduced** their energy demands, e.g. by being more energy efficient.

Pages 121-122 — Wave Basics

Q1 Waves transfer **energy** without transferring any **matter**.

Q2 a) Transverse — 2, Longitudinal — 1.

b) E.g. Transverse waves can travel in a vacuum but longitudinal waves cannot. / Vibrations in a transverse wave are perpendicular to the direction of travel/energy transfer, whereas in longitudinal waves they are parallel to the direction of travel/energy transfer.

Q3 a) A and C
b) A and B
c) A and C

Q4 vibrations are at 90° to the direction of energy transfer — T
produced by a slinky spring whose end is wiggled at 90° to the spring itself — T
ripples on water — T
electromagnetic radiation — T
vibrations are along the same direction as the energy transfer — L
sound waves — L
produced by a slinky spring whose end is pushed and pulled towards and away from the rest of the spring — L
they show areas of compression and rarefaction — L

Q5 a) metres
b) There are 25 waves per second.
c) A

Q6 $v = f \times \lambda$
$= 85 \times 4$
$= \mathbf{340\ m/s}$

Q7 2.5 Hz

Q8 a) He has drawn a wave with a wavelength of 4 m rather than 2 m.

b)

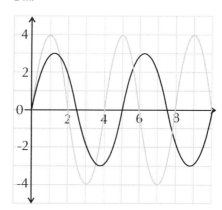

Q9 $\lambda = v \div f$
$= 300\ 000\ 000 \div 200\ 000$
$= \mathbf{1500\ m}$

Physics 1b — Electricity and Waves

Page 123 — Wave Properties

Q1 a) It is a construction line **at right angles** to the reflecting surface at the point of incidence.

b)

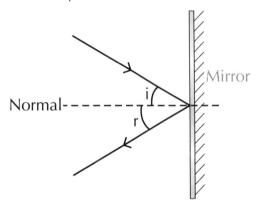

Q2 a) virtual
b) upright

Page 124 — Refraction and Diffraction

Q1 a) **All** waves spread out at the edges when they pass through a gap or **pass** an object — this is diffraction. The amount of diffraction **depends** on the size of the gap and the wavelength of the wave. Significant diffraction occurs when the wavelength of the wave is **the same** order of magnitude to the gap or obstacle

b)

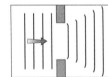

Q2 a) B
b) Waves don't refract when they're travelling along the normal.
c) When a wave changes direction as it crosses the boundary between two different substances.

Pages 125-126 — EM Waves and Communication

Q1 a)

Radio waves	Micro-waves	Infrared		Ultraviolet	X-rays	Gamma rays
1m-10^{4}m	10^{-2}m (1 cm)	10^{-5}m (0.01mm)	10^{-7}m	10^{-8}m	10^{-10}m	10^{-12}m

b) The energy of the waves **increases** from **left to right** across the table.
Q2 a) False — they all travel at the same speed.
b) False
c) False — they have the longest wavelength.
d) True
Q3 speed in a vacuum, they are both transverse waves
Q4 long-wave, short-wave, atmosphere, FM
Q5 A and B

Page 127 — EM Waves and Their Uses

Q1 a) Cameras, visible
b) more
Q2 Infrared radiation
Q3 a) Satellite TV uses **microwaves** to send signals. The signals from a transmitter are sent into space, where they're picked up by the satellite's receiver **dish**.
b) The satellite transmits the signal back to **Earth** in a different direction, where it is received by a satellite dish on the ground.
Q4 a) Microwaves
b) Their brain cells may be heated up and damaged.

Page 128 — Sound Waves

Q1 1 — When someone beats a drum, the skin on top of the drum vibrates.
2 — The vibration of the drum sets the air molecules next to it vibrating too.
3 — A series of compressions and rarefactions travel outwards through the air as a longitudinal wave.
4 — We hear the sound when the vibrations in the air reach our ears.
Q2 vibrate, high, low
Q3 a) A reflected sound wave.
b) The echo has to travel further than the original sound, so takes longer to reach your ears.
Q4 a) It gets quieter and eventually stops.
b) Sound can't travel in a vacuum because there are no particles to pass on the vibrations.

Pages 129-130 — The Origin of the Universe

Q1 The universe is getting **bigger**. All its galaxies seem to be moving **away from** each other (apart from a few very close ones).
Q2 a) The following two boxes should be ticked.
The wavelength of the sound seems longer to Francesca as the ambulance moves away.
As the ambulance moves away, the frequency of sound seems lower to Francesca.
b) As the ambulance moves towards Francesca, the frequency of the sound will seem **higher** to her and the wavelength of the sound will **decrease**.
c) Doppler effect
d) false, true
Q3 a) The light from distant galaxies has longer wavelengths than it should. (The light is shifted towards the red end of the electromagnetic spectrum.)
b) It shows that galaxies are moving away from us.
Q4 energy/matter, matter/energy, explosion, expand, Red-shift
Q5 It is a form of electromagnetic radiation that fills the universe.
Q6 a) False
b) True
c) True
Q7 E.g. It can't explain observed speeding up of the expansion of the universe. / It doesn't tell you anything about the universe before the Big Bang. / It doesn't explain what actually caused the explosion.

Physics 1b — Electricity and Waves

Pages 131-132 — Mixed Questions
— Physics 1b

Q1 The following three boxes should be ticked:
B represents ultraviolet radiation.
A represents infrared radiation.
A has the largest amplitude.

Q2 a) reflection

b)

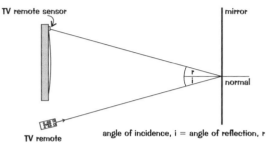

Q3 a) E.g. It doesn't produce any harmful gases. / It's reliable.

b) E.g. They won't run out. / They do less damage to the environment than non-renewables. / Low running costs.

c) Carbon capture and storage technology is used to collect CO_2 from fossil-fuel power stations before it is released into the atmosphere. This reduces the amount of CO_2 building up in the atmosphere and reduces the strength of the greenhouse effect.

Q4 a) diffraction

b) It will diffract the most when the gap is the same size as the wavelength. If the gap is much wider than the wavelength, it will only diffract a little.

c) Water molecules can absorb some wavelengths of microwave. If the water in question happens to be in your cells, e.g. brain cells, this may cause cell damage/your brain might start to cook.

d) CMBR, red-shift, expanding

Q5 a) i) E.g. Solar cells require little maintenance and no fuel, making them suitable for remote locations (where transporting fuel and arranging repairs would be difficult and expensive). Solar power is a renewable source of energy and won't pollute the island.

ii) E.g. The island is likely to be quite windy. Wind turbines are fairly cheap to install. As with solar power, wind power is renewable, doesn't cause pollution and doesn't require fuel.

b) Wave power — around the coastline, biomass — llama poo could be used to produce biofuel for burning. (Hydroelectric power might also be possible, depending on the island's geography and climate.)

ISBN 978 1 84146 705 4

9 781841 467054

SAFA45